Dedicated to my son, Andrew.
In memory of Andrew and Peter.

With special thanks to Lisa, Rob, Gordon, Charlie, Jo,
Rosie, Greig, Sandra, and Sarah.

The power of story

Encouraging a dialogue with children and giving them space to express their feelings from a young age and continue to do so as they grow, can have a really positive impact on their mental health.

Communicating with children and young people does not always mean tackling issues head on. It is much easier to work with a child indirectly using tools, distractions, and other mediums to facilitate engagement.

When a child is absorbed in a story their unconscious feelings and thoughts can flow more freely than when asked a direct question about themselves. This enchanting story of a teddy bear who faces lots of changes and emotions, can be used simply as a story book or to encourage a deeper level of engagement with a child or children as they relate to the bear's character.

A B Bear had been sitting on the shelf in the toy factory for a very long time. Every day from the warehouse racks, he watched as the machines picked out other toys and dropped them into baskets ready to be sent out to a lucky child who would be getting them for a birthday or Christmas present. He wondered to himself when was it going to be his turn?

Can you find AB Bear sitting on the shelf?

At night time, when the warehouse workers had all gone home, AB would look forward to climbing down off the shelf to see his other toy friends. He loved to spend time with the planes most of all. Sometimes they would give him a ride, flying past the other toys and making them jump!

4

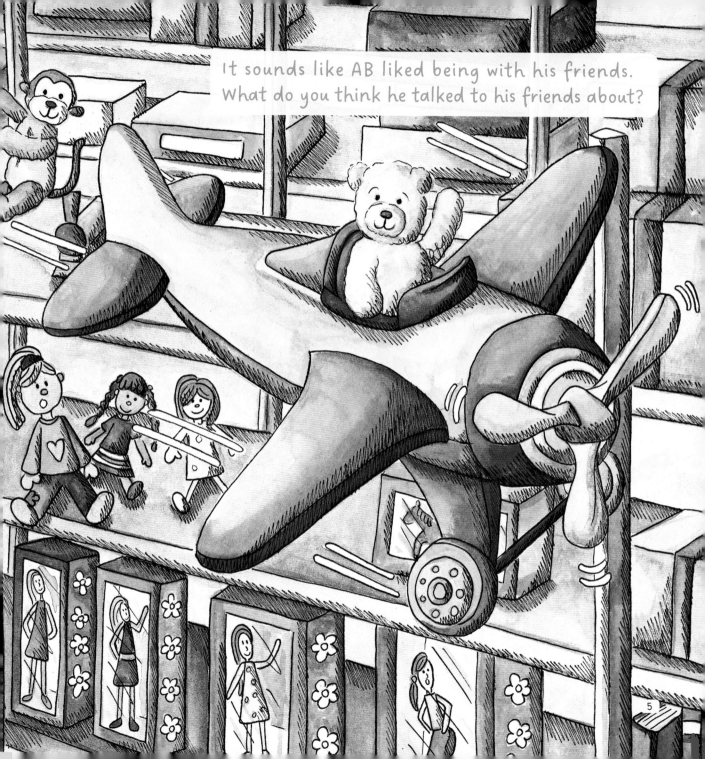

Suddenly, he was startled by a beeping sound from one of the pickers. Closer and closer it came. The long metal arm of the machine reached out to grab him. "Ouch!" he squealed, as he was grabbed by the leg, tipped upside down and dropped into a metal basket!

AB started to feel afraid. Where was he going? Who had picked him out? Would his new owner be a nice, kind child? Would they play with him or just leave him in a cupboard? Maybe, if he was really lucky he might be someone's extra special toy, being cuddled and kept warm at night. He would just have to wait and see.

Wow, that sounds like AB had lots of things to worry about. How do you think he felt?

AB waved goodbye to the other toys. As he passed the planes he gave them a 'thumbs up' to let them know he was okay. He would miss them a lot. "Perhaps I am going on an adventure" he said himself.

AB sounds excited, but at the same time he sounds sad having to leave his friends behind. It seems like sometimes we can have more than one feeling at the same time. What do you think?

AB was tipped out of the metal basket and into a cardboard box. In the box he saw some clothes that were about his size. It looked like a uniform and a hat." I wonder if they are for me?" he thought. He tried to look over the top of the box and could just see a postage label with an address on it. Sadly, he couldn't read it.

Oh, my goodness, it looks like AB may be soon wearing a uniform, and he doesn't know where he is going. It can be scary to do new things sometimes. How do you think he is feeling?

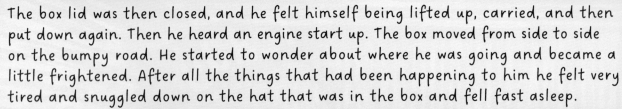

The box lid was then closed, and he felt himself being lifted up, carried, and then put down again. Then he heard an engine start up. The box moved from side to side on the bumpy road. He started to wonder about where he was going and became a little frightened. After all the things that had been happening to him he felt very tired and snuggled down on the hat that was in the box and fell fast asleep.

AB started to dream. He dreamt he was flying around the toy warehouse. He would fly up high and then down low, pretending to be a real pilot.

We all dream. If you could choose your dreams, what would they be about?

Suddenly, he was woken by a jolt. Everything went very quiet. AB felt the box being lifted up again. He heard a door creak open. A man said, "I have a parcel for Station Commander, Group Captain Hill." "Thank you, that's me," said Group Captain Hill. "Just place the box there on the floor please with Squadron Leader Smith. Children would you like to help open it?"

AB sat very still. "A captain? Am I on a ship?" AB wondered. There was a tearing sound as the box was opened and AB found himself staring into the eyes of a lady and two little children. "Welcome to your new home. We have been waiting for you," said the lady. My name is Squadron Leader Miss Smith. Now, let's see how these fit," pointing to the little green uniform and hat that has been in the box with AB.

It sounds like AB is just like us; sometimes things change and we move home or school and it can feel a bit scary. Sometimes though change can be exciting as we get to meet new people. How do you think AB was feeling now?

AB was lifted out of the box and felt himself being squeezed into his new outfit - it was like the uniforms that his friends the toy pilots wore in the toy warehouse. He looked at a reflection of himself in the window. "This is brilliant," he thought. "I look like a real pilot." The children saw him and smiled. "You look amazing," they both said at the same time.

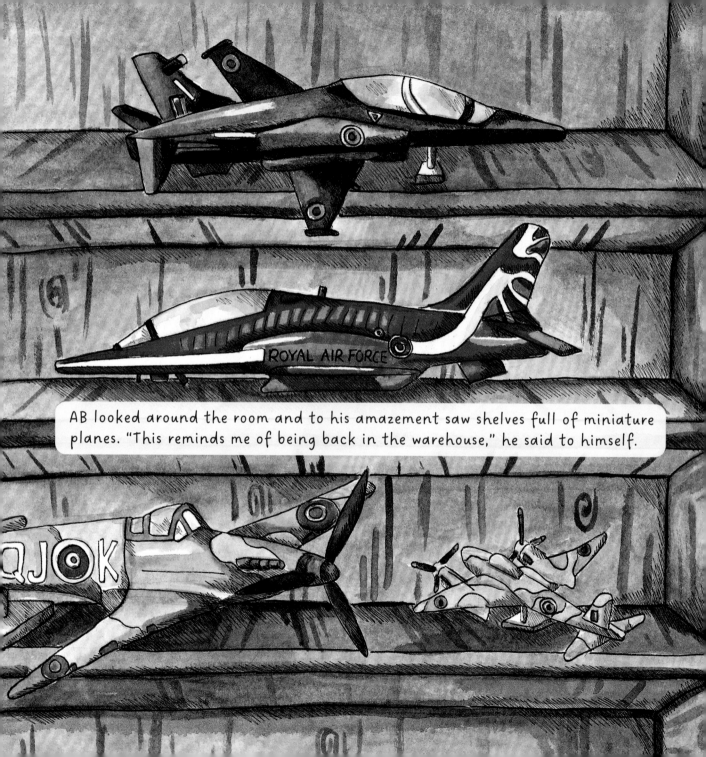

AB looked around the room and to his amazement saw shelves full of miniature planes. "This reminds me of being back in the warehouse," he said to himself.

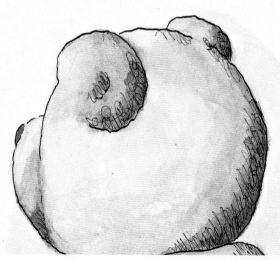

AB must have felt very excited in his new outfit and with all the planes, although they could have reminded him of the friends that he had left behind. What do you think?

Group Captain Hill picked him up and carried him into the room next door where a doctor was waiting for him. "Hi Doctor Saba, our new mascot has arrived. Say hello to AB Bear. He's here for his medical before he's allowed to go up." "Okay," replied Doctor Saba. "Hello AB, let's have a look at you then."

AB sat on the desk and was prodded and poked until it felt like all the stuffing was going to come out of him! Doctor Saba connected him to a machine that made noises and then put him on the scales to be weighed. He was very relieved when the doctor said, "Yes, he's passed the test and he's ready for action!"

Goodness, all these new things that are happening to AB. How do you think he is feeling right now?

"Wow, ready for action" thought AB. "What does that mean?" AB became a little scared. Group Captain Hill carried him out into the yard. "Meet your new Mascot," he said to a group of pilots that had gathered. "This is AB - he's just passed his medical and is going up for his first flight this afternoon!"

AB couldn't believe his ears. No longer was he just going to sit in toy planes and fly around a warehouse at night - he was going to fly in a real plane with real pilots! "Okay, who's taking him out? Ricko, Lisa, Rob?"

"I will, Sir," said Flight Lieutenant Ricko. "He can come out for a quick spin in my Hawk plane this afternoon. I will take him to look at the beautiful Welsh countryside." "Gosh, I feel like I am dreaming," thought AB. "Only yesterday, I was stuck on a shelf and wondering if I would ever get to see the outside world, but here I am today, about to go up in a real-life plane. I cannot believe it!"

Things really seemed to be looking up for AB. What do you think was making him feel better?

AB was taken into the flight training room and was put in a chair with the other pilots. They were being given their instructions for the training session. It all looked very complicated. They had maps on their desks and were writing things. Once finished, they gathered their papers and went to their locker rooms to prepare.

Once all the pilots had changed into their outfits, they went outside to the hangar where the planes were lined up. A group of engineers were checking them over. "All sorted, Sir," said Jimbo, who had given them the final nod. "Ready for take-off."

"Thanks, good to go, everyone," said Ricko. "Right then AB, let's see how you are on your first training flight. I doubt you have ever flown in a plane before." Little did Ricko know about AB's flights in the warehouse. Ricko climbed into the cockpit and placed AB beside the controls. "Let's get your belt on. If you feel unwell make sure you put on your oxygen mask," he told AB.

30

That must have been nice for AB, Ricko certainly seems to be helping AB feel welcome and safe. How do you think AB felt?

31

Suddenly, AB heard a big roar and felt a huge shudder go through the plane as it moved forward towards the runway. Faster and faster, it went. Soon he was in the air, racing towards the big blue sky. "This is amazing!" he thought.

AB whooshed through the clouds, swerving past mountains, racing low over the fields. They soared higher and higher as the planes turned and twisted and circled around each other. They finished with a loop-the-loop as they came in past the control tower to land.

AB was carried out of the plane and faced a waiting crowd. "I hope you enjoyed that AB, although we haven't finished yet," said Flight Lieutenant Ricko. "Look what we have got for you," he said, showing AB a little blue box. Ricko opened the box up. Inside was a small, shiny badge.

Ricko took it out of the box and pinned it onto AB's beret. "Well, if you're going to be the Station Mascot, you've got to look the part of an RAF pilot," he said.

The children that had watching AB in the plane started to clap. AB smiled to himself. "What a few days I have had. Not long ago I had to say goodbye to my friends in the toy warehouse and I was afraid as I didn't know where I was going. Now I have more friends - and I have even flown in a plane with a real pilot!"

"He can talk!" squealed Squadron Leader Miss Smith who nearly fell backwards in shock.

"You no longer need to be afraid," said Ricko. "If ever there is something that worries you or makes you sad, remember to tell an adult that you trust, or talk to one of us and we will help." "I promise I will," replied AB, as he started to imagine what his next adventure was going to be.

THE END

Wow what a lovely story, it seems that AB had to face lots of scary things, and sad things, like saying goodbye to his friends. We all go through times like this. Some days we feel scared or sad, and some days we feel happy.

Can you think of all the feelings AB had in the story and if you felt those feelings sometimes too?

Think of an adventure that AB might go on next.

Why not become a friend of AB and be a member of the
BEAR FORCE BUDDIES?

To be a member all you have to do is read this book or ask someone to read it with you and remember the things below.
1.   Being brave includes speaking to an adult you trust if you are feeling sad or frightened.
2.   Always be kind to others who you think may be sad or frightened.
3.   If you think someone is unhappy, tell an adult - like a teacher, as they may be able to help them.
4.   Sometimes when things change it can be scary. Remember though that change can also lead to exciting things.

Why not ask someone to download the Bear Force Buddies Membership Certificate from the Bear Force website: www.bearforce.org.uk Here you will find other information that you might like too. Copy or trace the Bear Force Buddies badge at the top of this page and write your name in the space at the bottom.
Why not encourage your friends to become members or ask your teacher if everyone in your class can join and all be members of the Bear Force Buddies?

www.bearforce.org.uk

A website for children providing help and advice,
written in way that children can understand.

Other helpful contact details for children:

Childline is available day or night, 7 days a week.
Telephone 0800 1111
www.childline.org.uk
If you are deaf or hard of hearing telephone 0800 400 222
In an emergency telephone 999
...
Advice for children, young people and families about bereavement, grief and loss
www.thedoveservice.org.uk
...
Advice for children, teenagers and adults on many matters
associated with young people's mental health
www.youngminds.org.uk
...
For children affected by violence at home
www.thehideout.org.uk
Telephone 0808 2000 247
...
If you or your parents or carers want advice on gender dysphoria
www.mermaids.org.uk